The Shoe Shiner

A Timmy Bumbleburke Tale

by

Ricky J. McRoskey

Illustrations

Ewa Krepsztul

The Shoe Shiner
A Timmy Bumbleburke Tale
2016 First Printing
Copyright © 2016 by April Rain Publishing

ISBN: 9780982322703

The Shoe Shiner / by Ricky J. McRoskey; illustrated by Ewa Krepsztul.

Summary: Young Timmy Bumbleburke wants to start his own business and at the advice of his business-savvy father, he prays to Saint Joseph. Immediately Timmy is thrust into the world of first-century Galilee, in a small, oak-smelling workshop alongside the master craftsman. Over the course of the day, Timmy learns from this strong and gentle mentor the secret to great work—and has the most memorable dinner of his life. In this book, author and business writer Ricky J. McRoskey teams up with award-winning illustrator Ewa Krepsztul to deliver a unique children's book and an engaging story aimed at inspiring young future entrepreneurs to pursue their dreams, and to integrate faith in business, in all they do.

Text
Ricky J. McRoskey

Illustrations, Cover Design and Layout
Ewa Krepsztul

Published by
April Rain Publishing
www.AprilRainPublishing.com

For Dad, a true Joseph

My name is **Timmy Bumbleburke,**
And I sure have a tale for you,
One day I went with dad to work
And saw a man who shines your shoes.

His hands were fast, the shoes, they glowed!
And after that he got his due.
I asked my pops, "Dad, do you know..."
"Could I make money shining shoes?"

"Of course," he said real quick. "You can.
Of that I am extremely sure.
You can be a businessman,
A Bumbleburke entrepreneur."

Knowing that my dad is smart,
And runs a business very well,
I asked him, "Now, how best to start
A shoe-shine bus'ness? **Dad, do tell!"**

"There's lots and lots of things to learn,
And lots of things that you should know,
But one thing that I've found works best,
Is praying to a saint, **Saint Joe**."

"Who's he?" I asked. My dad replied,
"A carpenter, a man of mirth,
But best of all he's known, my child,
As **dad of Jesus here on earth**."

"He watches over families,
Especially those who work all day.
**Whenever you need help with work,
Listen to what he has to say**."

That night I prayed to this great saint,
"St. Joseph, teach me where to start —
What will I need to do to shine?
How can I shine those shoes with heart?"

And then he came, at once, he stood
Before my eyes and smiled at me
And told me to come follow him
To a **small town in Galilee...**

Within a flash we stood amidst
A shop with wood piled here and there.
The sawdust filled the air like mist,
With chairs and tables everywhere!

"I'll need your help," he said to me.
"I've worked on this since last weekend.
A very special piece, you see."
"For whom?" I asked. He said, "A friend."

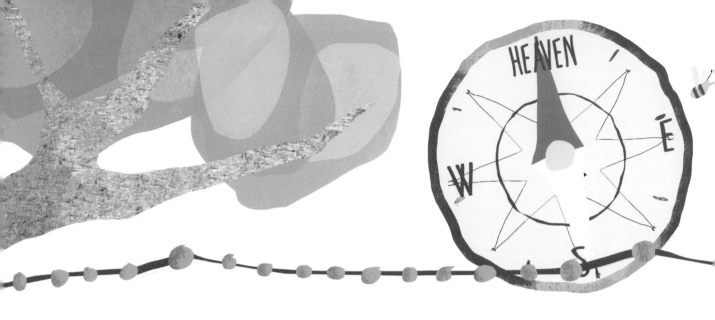

"But first thing's first," St. Joseph said,
"Before all else we have to PLAN,
So pray that God will guide your head
And thoughts before you move your hand."

"Next thing, we pray for ENERGY
That we might have the strength to move,
And lift or sand or shine or see,
Whatever God calls us to do."

"Dear God, please bless our hands and feet,
Sustain us as we do perspire.
Please give to us your gifts of STRENGTH
And COURAGE when our hands grow tired."

And next, we pray for PATIENCE, which
Is hard to have when things go wrong.
"Dear God, please give us calm and grit,
To not be vexed when days are long."

At times wood cracks, or things can break,
And then we have to start anew,
But that is work, it's what it takes,
To make a lovely chair or two.

So now, we're close to finishing,
But first we must learn how to stain
And this is where I must admit,
My neighbor John is better trained.

He'll teach us how, John's very good,
He'll teach us how to make it glow
And that is why you always should
Know that there's much you don't yet know.

"Dear God, give us humility,
In all we do, in all we move.
Give us, dear God, tranquility,
Please help us constantly improve."

And now, my boy, we're done with this,
So thanks is what we humbly give
To God; for work, for food, for health,
For giving us the means to live!"

He said, "Now please come follow me —
It's time to eat; our day is done.
My fav'rite part of every day
Is dinner with my wife and son."

And so we went right out the shop,
Into the kitchen, where they were.
Fresh bread sat on the tabletop,
And cheese and greens and soup du jour.

"My boy, please meet my wife Mary,
And son, who sits there in her lap."
"Please won't you stay for now?" said she,
"You must be hungry after that."

We talked and laughed for hours, and
The meal—delicious! Hearty! Fun!
Then Mary looked to me and asked,
"Now would you like to hold my son?"

I held the babe, whose hair was gold,
His smile was warm as winter fleece,
And from His gorgeous eyes there gleamed,
A look of pure, undying peace."

O Peace! That was the perfect word
Describing Mary, Joseph, and
Their son, whose smile could light the world.
I saw their peace and love first-hand.

And then St. Joseph rose and said
We had just one more thing to do,
"Let's tackle one more task," he said.
"Complete our work, now, me and you."

Back in the shop he grabbed the wood,
And hammered for a blink or two,
So then I asked, "Saint Joe, what's that?"
"A box," he said, "for shining shoes."

"Just like I saw with dad," I said.
And then St. Joseph spoke anew,
"Son, do you like it? Good, I'm glad,
Because this is my gift to you."

"Now go and shine some worn-down shoes
And **pray to God to bless your work.**
Remember that I'm here for you,
God bless you, Timmy Bumbleburke."

With that he left and soon I found
Myself at home upon my bed,
With my new shoebox on the ground.
Then I recalled what Dad had said.

"He watches over families,
Especially those who work all day.
Whenever you need help with work,
Listen to what he has to say."

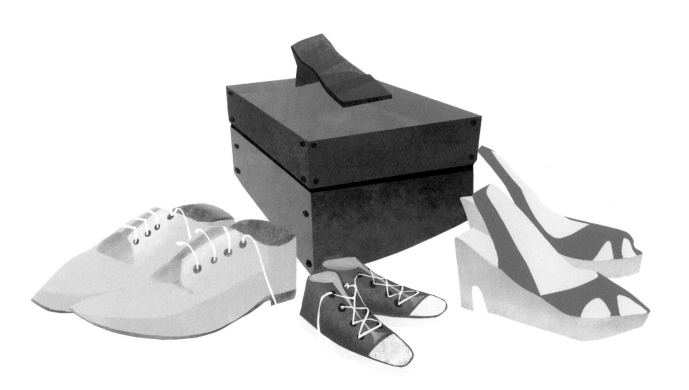

can You

figure it out?

This is a special section for inquiring young minds.

Can you figure out the meaning behind
the different symbols, plants and animals
used on pages 18 and 19?

Go back to Pages 18 and 19, read St. Joseph's advice,
and see if you can identify the meaning behind the
different images that surround those pages.

Then check your answers here. ⟶

INDEX

ANTS

Ants are hard workers. They put all of their effort into carrying every bread crumb or grain, and they understand the importance of working together. They don't seem to realize how small they are; they're too busy accomplishing something. It's the same attitude we should bring to our businesses—and our spiritual lives.

Go to the ant, you sluggard. Consider its ways, and be wise. - Proverbs 6:6

OAK TREE

The massive oak tree begins as an acorn the size of your thumb. It takes years and years of watering and sunshine to grow to its enormous size. It reminds us that greatness doesn't come overnight. Whether it's an oak tree, a project, or our spiritual lives, it's important for us to remember the virtue of patience.

Happy are those who follow not the counsel of the wicked...they are like a tree planted near running water, which yields its fruit in due season. - Psalm 1

LION

The lion symbolizes strength and courage. We need these virtues in anything we do—the strength to keep going when we are tired, and the courage to do what is right, no matter how difficult it may be. Like a lion, Christ gives us these gifts if we ask for His help in our work.

The wicked flee when no one pursues, but the righteous are bold as a lion. - Proverbs 28:1

ROSARY

The Rosary is the most beautiful and powerful prayer we have to Mary, Christ's mother and Joseph's wife. When we ask for her help and guidance, she leads us closer to Jesus and presents our prayers to Him. Jesus always listens to His mom!

When Jesus saw his mother and the disciple whom he loved standing nearby, he said to his mother, "Woman, behold, your son!" Then he said to the disciple, "Behold, your mother!" - John 19:26-27

COMPASS

A compass helps a traveler find the right path. In the same way, God has given us many "compasses" that point us to Christ and to Heaven: the Church and its teachings, Scripture, the sacraments, the Blessed Mother, the saints, and the Holy Mass.

Jesus answered, "I am the Way, the Truth, and the Life. No one comes to the Father except through me." -John 14:6

BEES

Bees are symbols of perseverance in doing good. They work tirelessly to make honey, which is not only sweet but can also be used as medicine. If we offer our work up to God, we too can put our energy into doing something good, whether making a chair, cleaning the house, or brightening someone's day.

How sweet are your words to my taste, sweeter than honey to my mouth! -Psalm 119

SUN

The sun gives us light and energy. Without the sun, we could not live, plants would not grow, and the whole earth would wither and die. Jesus is like the sun. He is the Light of the World. He gives us life and is the source of all growth. We rely on Him in our work just as we need the sun in our daily lives.

And Jesus spoke to them, saying, "I am the Light of the World. Whoever follows me will not walk in darkness, but will have the light of life." -John 8:12

POOL OF WATER

Water represents refreshment, purity, and peace. Just as we might go to a pool of water to clean ourselves, the sacrament of baptism washes away our sins. And just as our bodies need water when we are thirsty, our souls need Jesus to be refreshed and renewed.

Beside restful waters He leads me; He refreshes my soul. -Psalm 23

Ewa Krepsztul is an award-winning illustrator, fine artist and graphic designer whose wondrous sensitivity for visual communication is equal to none. She lives in Connecticut with her husband and two children.

Ricky McRoskey is a communications strategist for a New York-based firm. A graduate of the University of Notre Dame and the Columbia Graduate School of Journalism, he is an exceptionally gifted writer who has written for *Catholic Business Journal*, *BusinessWeek* and *Business Insider*. He lives in Connecticut with his wife and three children.

CPSIA information can be obtained at www.ICGtesting.com
Printed in the USA
LVIW01n0041160517
534665LV00010B/153